Greatest Hits

Wise Publications
London/New York/Paris/Sydney/Copenhagen/Berlin/Madrid/Tokyo

Exclusive Distributors:
Music Sales Limited
8/9 Frith Street, London W1D 3JB, England.
Music Sales Pty Limited
120 Rothschild Avenue, Rosebery, NSW 2018, Australia.

Order No. AM973357
ISBN 0-7119-9248-7
This book © Copyright 2002 by Wise Publications

Compiled by Nick Crispin
Music arranged by Stephen Duro & Roger Day
Music processed by Enigma Music Production Services
Cover photographs courtesy of London Features International

Printed and bound in Malta by Interprint Limited

Your Guarantee of Quality
As publishers, we strive to produce every book to the highest commercial standards.
The music has been freshly engraved and the book has been carefully designed to minimise
awkward page turns and to make playing from it a real pleasure.
Particular care has been given to specifying acid-free, neutral-sized paper made from pulps
which have not been elemental chlorine bleached. This pulp is from farmed sustainable forests
and was produced with special regard for the environment.
Throughout, the printing and binding have been planned to ensure a sturdy, attractive publication
which should give years of enjoyment.
If your copy fails to meet our high standards, please inform us and we will gladly replace it.

www.musicsales.com

Against All Odds
(Take A Look At Me Now)

Words & Music by Phil Collins

Moderately slow

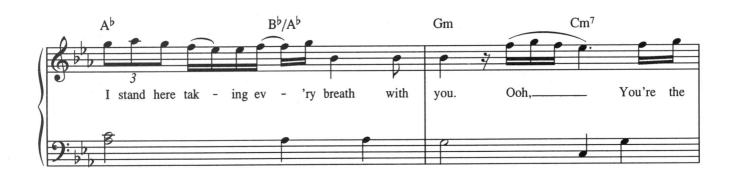

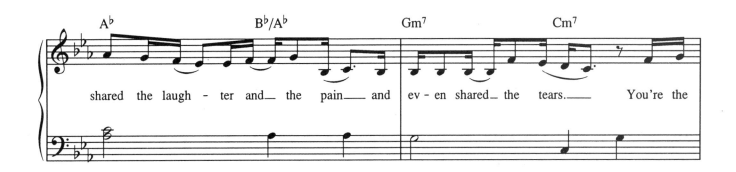

shared the laugh - ter and__ the pain__ and ev - en shared__ the tears.__ You're the

on- ly one who real- ly knew me__ at all.__ So take a look at me now,__

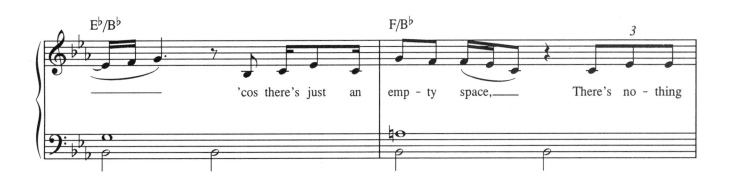

__ 'cos there's just an emp - ty space,__ There's no - thing

left__ here__ to re - mind__ me, just the mem -

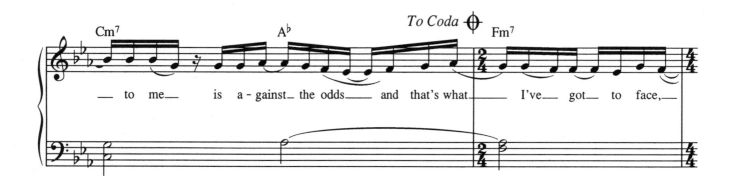

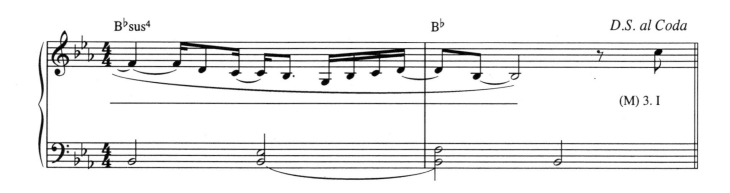

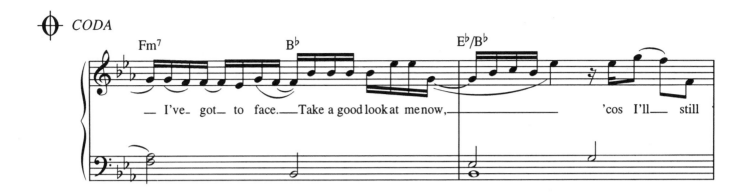

— I've_ got_ to face.__Take a good look at me now,_____ 'cos I'll_ still

be stand - ing here._____ And you com - in' back__

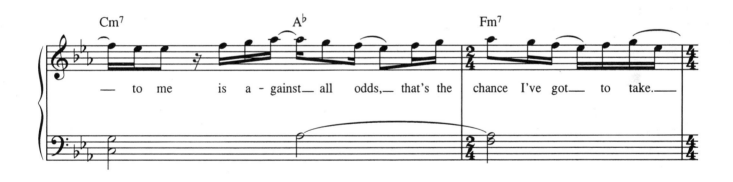

— to me is a - gainst_ all odds,_ that's the chance I've got__ to take.__

— (M)Chance I've got to take. Got to take._____

Take   a   look   at   me   now.___   (F) Take   a   look   at   me   now.___

_____   (M) Take   a   look   at   me   now._____

Verse 3:

I wish I could just make you turn around
Turn around and see me cry
There's so much I need to say to you
So many reasons why
You're the only one
Who really knew me at all.

So take a look at me now,
Well there's just an empty space.
There's nothing left here to remind me,
Just the memory of your face.
Oh take a look at me now,
So there's just an empty space.
But to wait for you is all I can do,
And that's what I've got to face.

Emotion

Words & Music by Barry Gibb & Robin Gibb

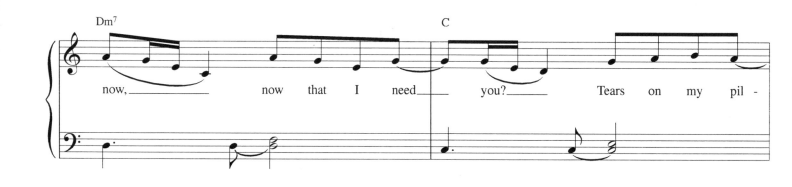

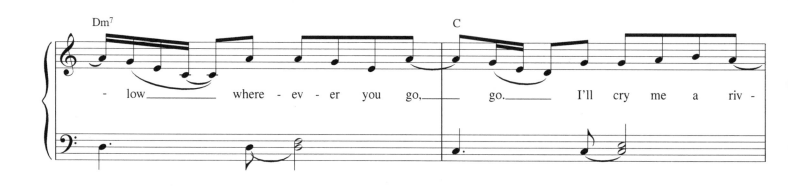

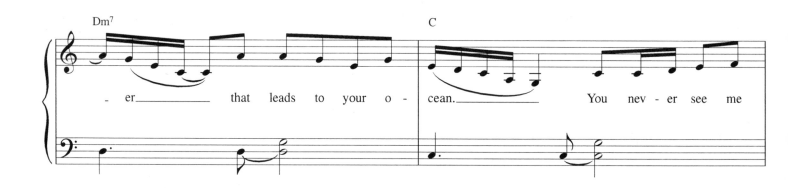

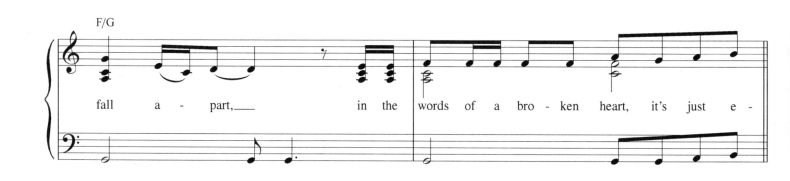

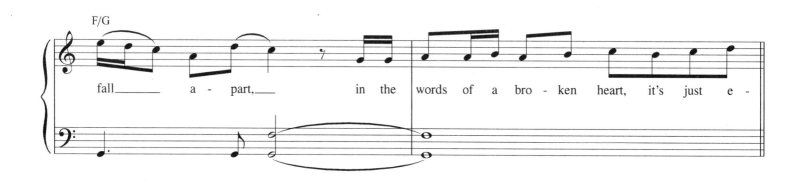

No - bo - dy left in this world to hold me tight, no - bo - dy____ to hold

me, in the world to kiss good - night, no - bo - dy_____ to kiss____

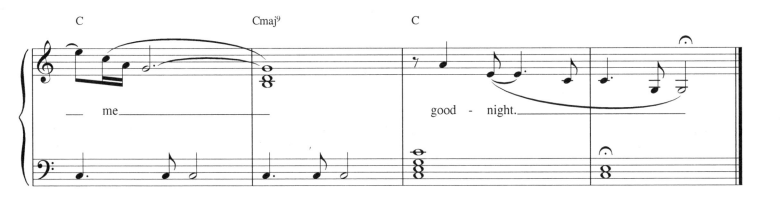

____ me_____ good - night.____

Verse 2:
I'm there at your side,
I'm part of all the things you are
But you've got a part of someone else
You've got to go find your shining star.

And where are you now *etc.*

Breathless

Words & Music by R.J. Lange, Andrea Corr,
Caroline Corr, Sharon Corr & Jim Corr

Moderately

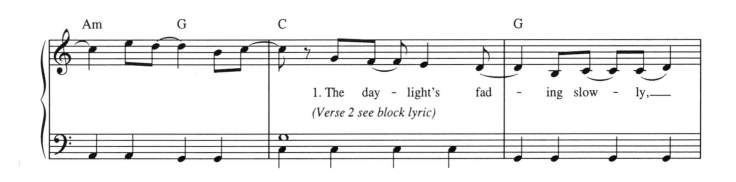

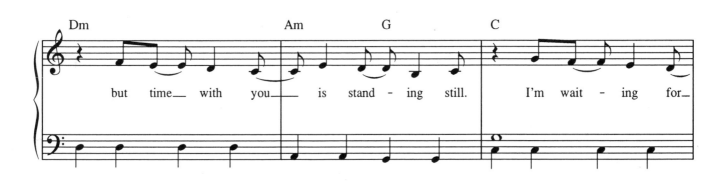

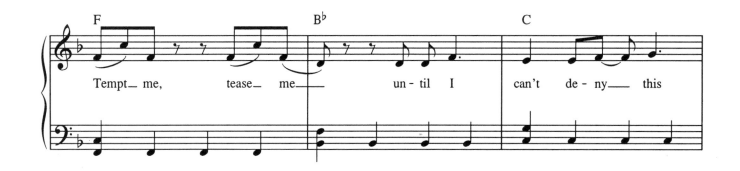

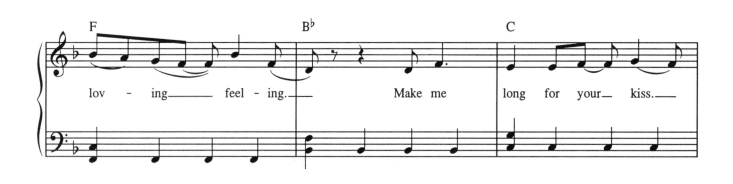

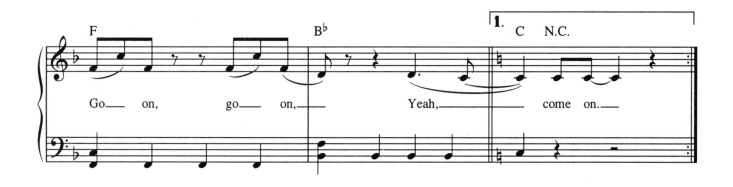

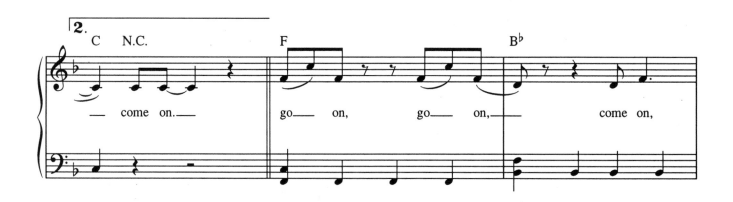

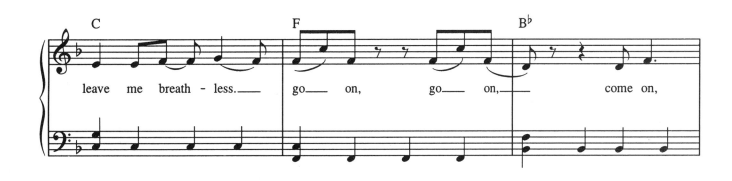

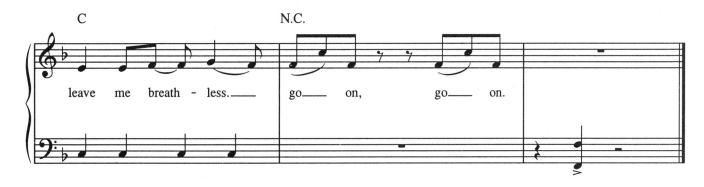

Verse 2:

And if there's no tomorrow
And all we have is here and now
I'm happy just to have you
You're all the love I need somehow
It's like a dream
Although I'm not asleep
And I never want to wake up
Don't lose it, don't leave it.

So go on, go on *etc.*

Can't Get You Out Of My Head

Words & Music by Cathy Dennis & Rob Davis

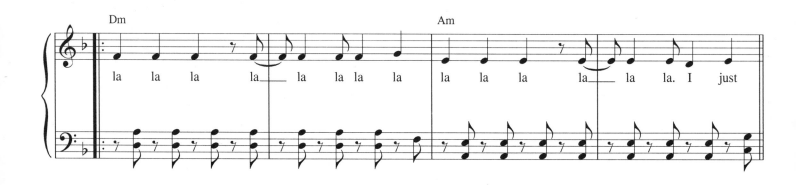

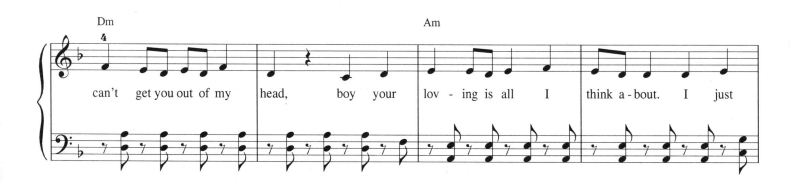

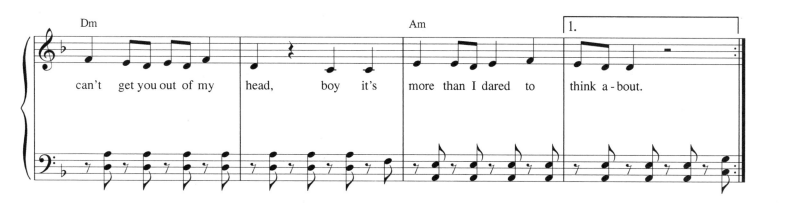

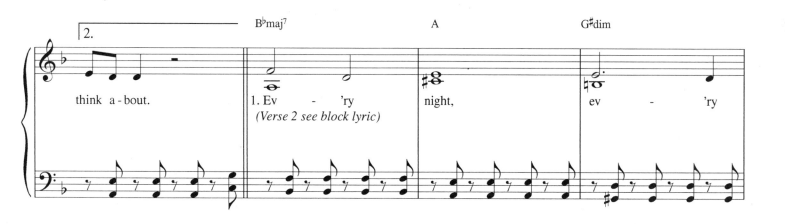

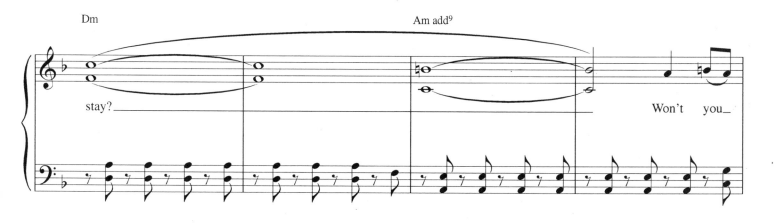

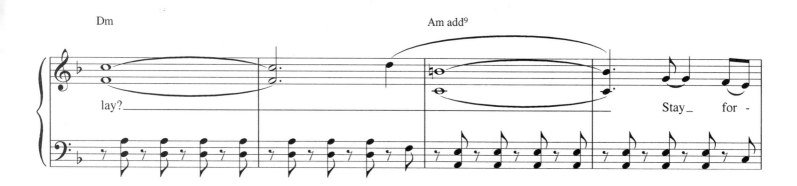

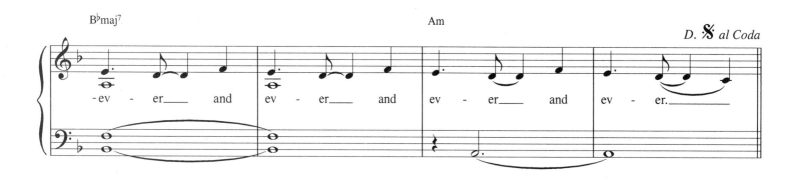

 CODA

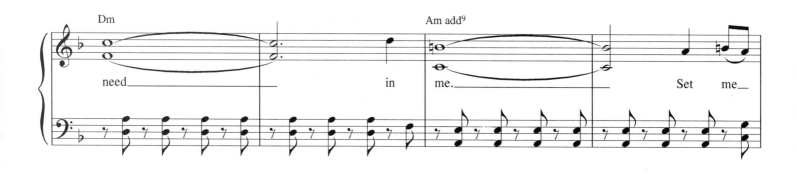

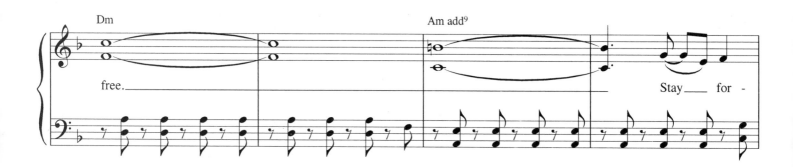

20

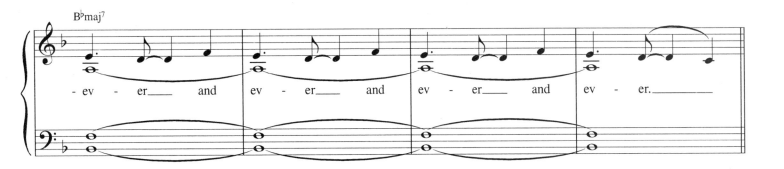

B♭maj⁷ ... -ev - er____ and ev - er____ and ev - er____ and ev - er._____

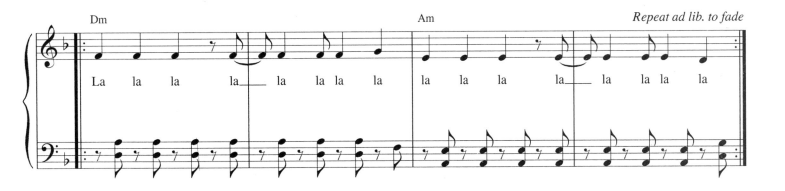

Dm ... Am ... *Repeat ad lib. to fade*

La la la la____ la la la la la la la la____ la la la la

Verse 2:
There's a dark secret in me
Don't leave me locked in your heart
Set me free *etc.*

Don't Stop Movin'

Words & Music by Simon Ellis, Sheppard Solomon & S Club 7

Moderately

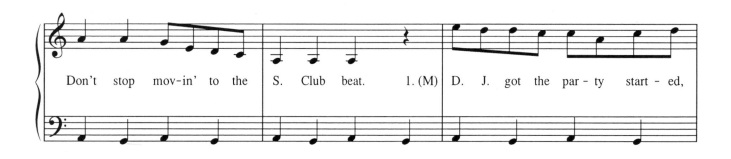

- -zy world, but to - night's the right si - tu - a - tion. Don't get left be - hind.

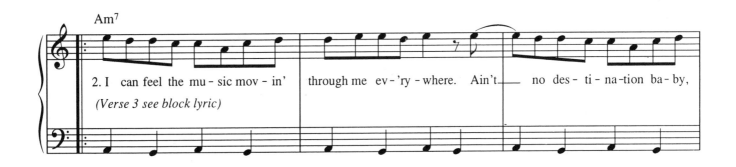

2. I can feel the mu - sic mov - in' through me ev - 'ry - where. Ain't no des - ti - na - tion ba - by,
(Verse 3 see block lyric)

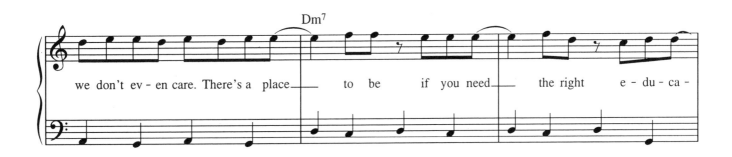

we don't ev - en care. There's a place to be if you need the right e - du - ca -

- tion. Let it take you there. (F) And just go with the ma - gic, ba - by.

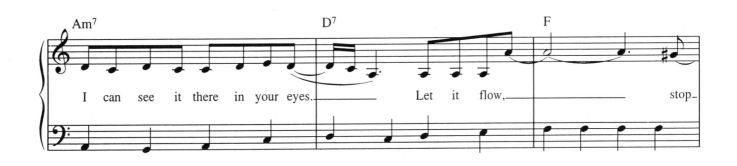

I can see it there in your eyes. Let it flow, stop

23

the wait - ing, right here on the dance floor is where you got - ta let it go. Don't

stop mov - in', can you feel the mu - sic? D. J.'s got us go - in' a - round,

round. Don't stop mov - in', find your own way to it. Lis -

- ten to the mu - sic. Tak - ing you to pla - ces that you've nev - er been be - fore, ba - by now.

Don't stop mov in' to the fun-ky, fun-ky beat. Don't stop mov in' to the fun-ky, fun-ky beat.

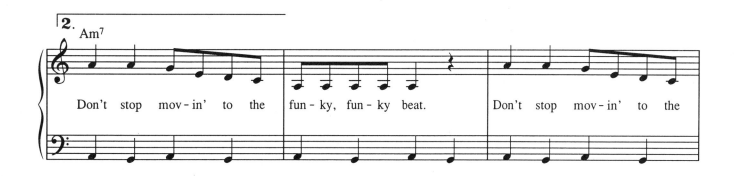

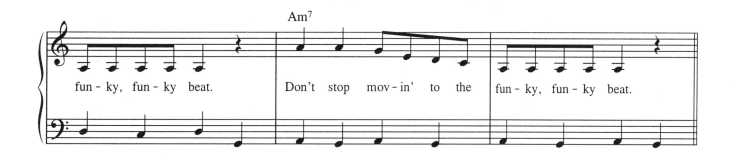

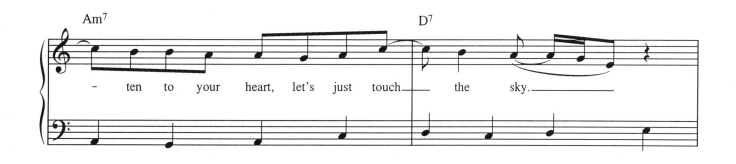

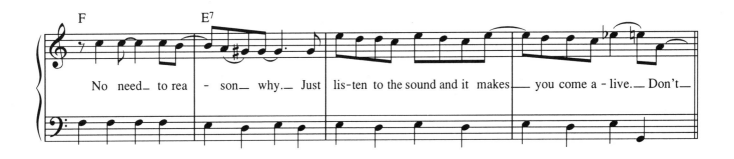

Verse 3:

You can touch the moment almost feel it in the air
Don't know where we're goin' baby we don't even care
Ain't no mystery, just use your imagination
Let it take you there
Just go with your magic baby
I can see it there in your eyes
Let it flow, stop the waiting, right here on the dance floor
Is where you gotta let it go.

Don't stop movin' can you feel the music *etc.*

Evergreen

Words & Music by Jörgen Elofsson, Per Magnusson & David Kreuger

rall.

Verse 2:
Touch like an angel,
Like velvet to my skin.
And I wonder, I wonder why you wanna stay the night,
What you're dreaming, what's behind.
Don't tell me, but it feels like love.

Eternity

Words & Music by Robbie Williams & Guy Chambers

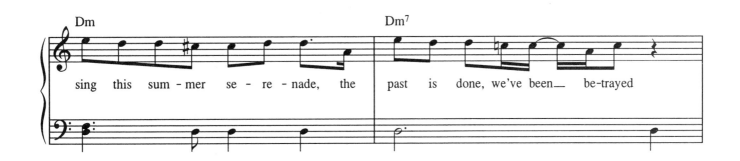

sing this sum-mer se-re-nade, the past is done, we've been— be-trayed

it's true.— Some-one said the truth will out and

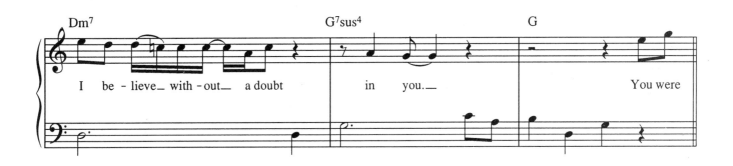

I be - lieve— with-out— a doubt in you.— You were

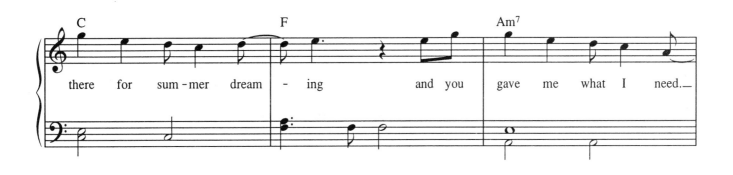

there for sum-mer dream - ing and you gave me what I need.—

— And I hope you'll find your free - dom— for e-ter-ni-

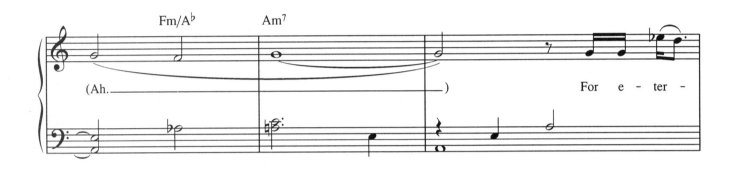

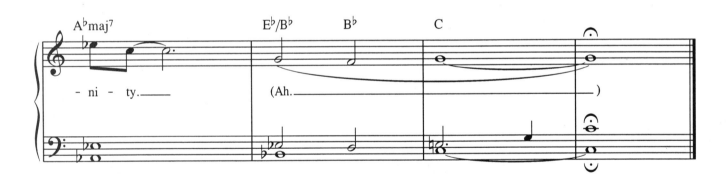

Verse 2:

Yesterday when you were walking
We talked about your Mum and Dad
What they did that made you happy
What they did that made you sad
We sat and watched the sun go down
Picked a star before we lost the moon
Youth is wasted on the young
Before you know, it's come and gone too soon.

You were there for summer dreaming   *etc.*

Have A Nice Day

Words & Music by Kelly Jones

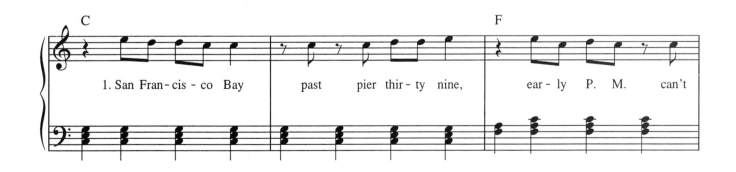

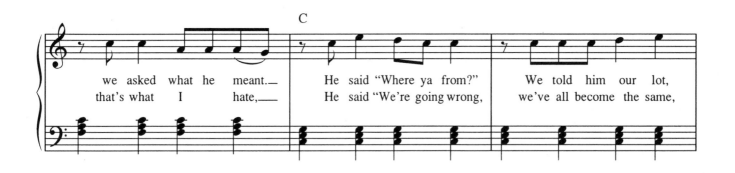

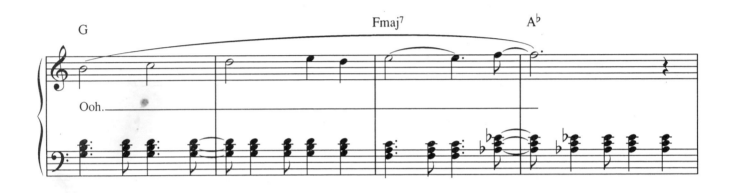

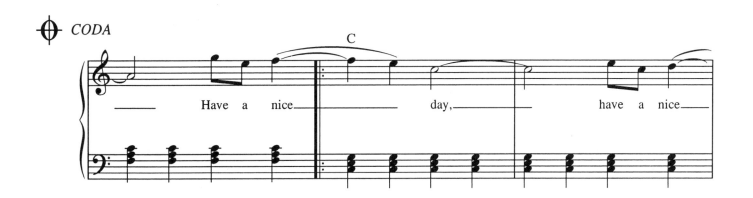

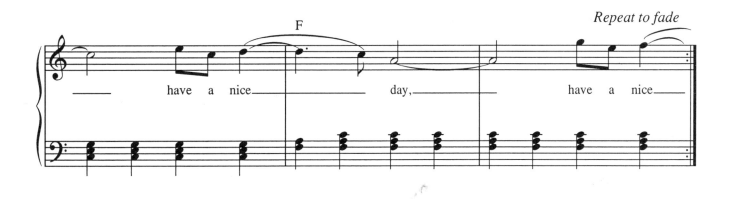

Verse 4:

Swim in the ocean
That be my dish
I drive around all day
And kill processed fish.
It's all money gum
No artists anymore
You're only in it now
To make more, more, more.
So have a nice day *etc.*

Pure And Simple

Words & Music by Tim Hawes, Pete Kirtley & Alison Clarkson

Moderately

1. You been say-ing I'm dri-ving you cra-zy *(Verse 2 see block lyric)* and I have-n't been a-round for you late-ly,

but I have a few things on my mind.

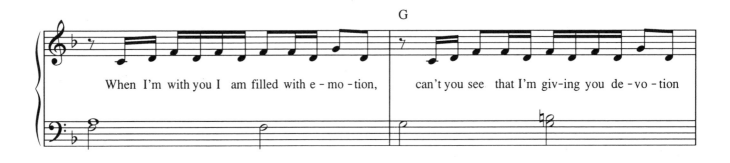

When I'm with you I am filled with e-mo-tion, can't you see that I'm giv-ing you de-vo-tion

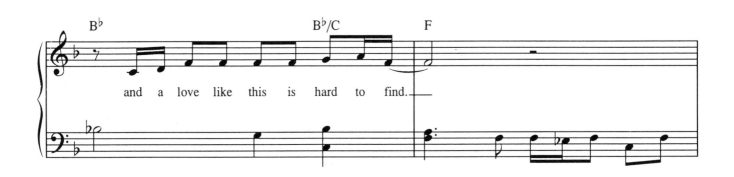

and a love like this is hard to find.

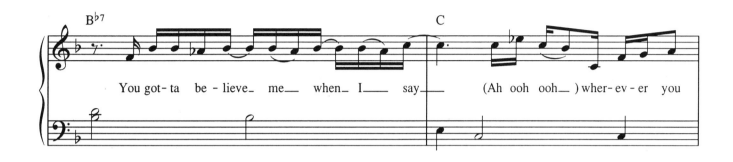

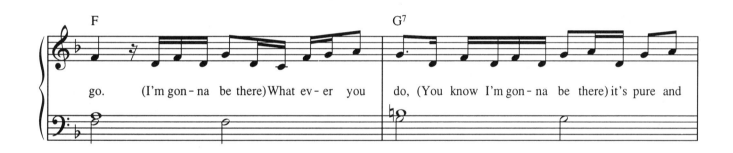

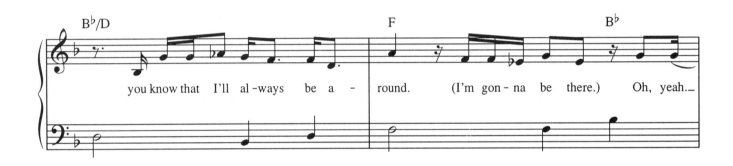

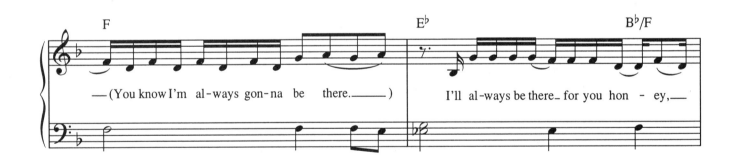

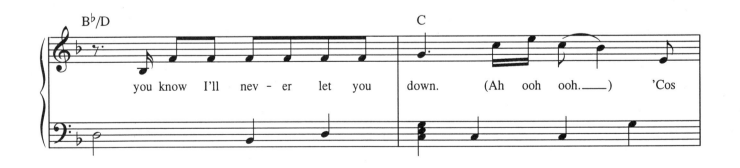

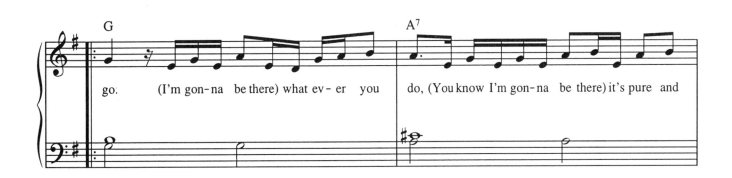

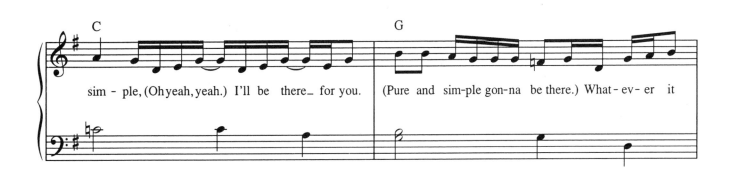

takes, (I'm gon-na be there) I swear it's true,__ (You know I'm gon-na be there) it's pure and

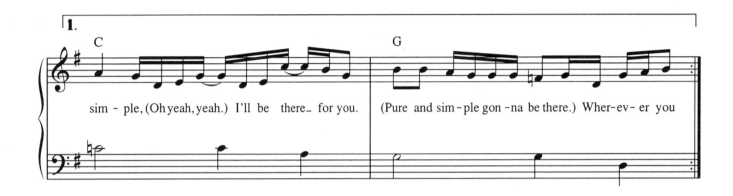

sim - ple, (Oh yeah, yeah.) I'll be there_ for you. (Pure and sim-ple gon-na be there.) Wher-ev- er you

sim - ple, (Oh yeah, yeah.)_ I'll be there_ for you. (Pure and sim-ple gon-na be there.)

Verse 2:

I'll be there through the stormiest weather
Always trying to make things a bit better
And I know I gotta try and get through to you
You can love me in a way like no other
But the situation's taking you under
So you need to tell me now what you wanna do.

I know I've been walking around in daze (Baby, baby)
You gotta believe me when I say (Ah, ooh, ooh)

Wherever you go *etc*.

She

Words by Herbert Kretzmer
Music by Charles Aznavour

Moderately slow

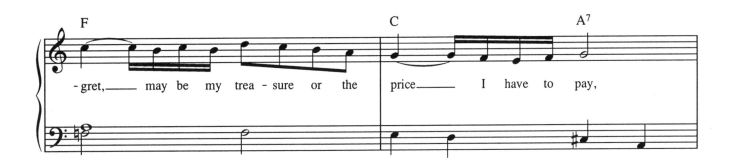

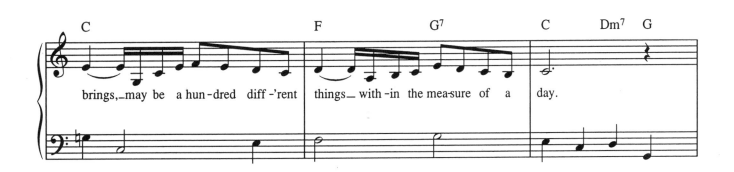

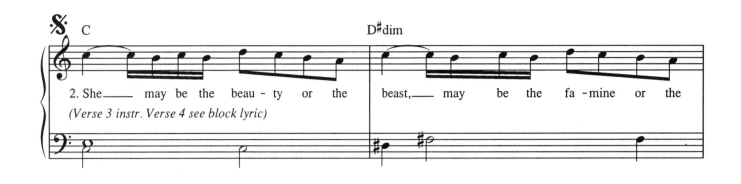

2. She____ may be the beau - ty or the beast,____ may be the fa - mine or the
(Verse 3 instr. Verse 4 see block lyric)

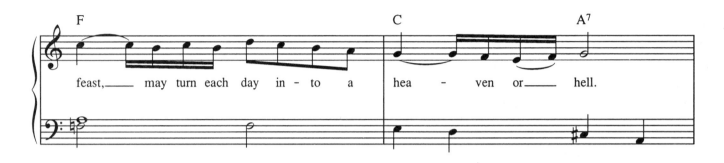

feast,____ may turn each day in - to a hea - ven or____ hell.

She____ may be the mir - ror of my dreams____ a smile re - flec - ted in a

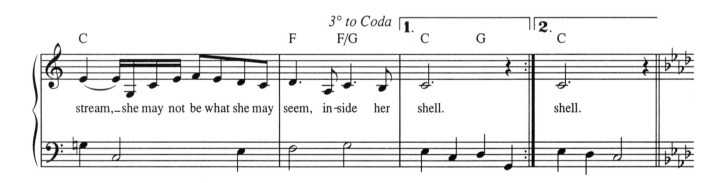

3° to Coda **1.**   **2.**

stream,____she may not be what she may seem, in - side her shell. shell.

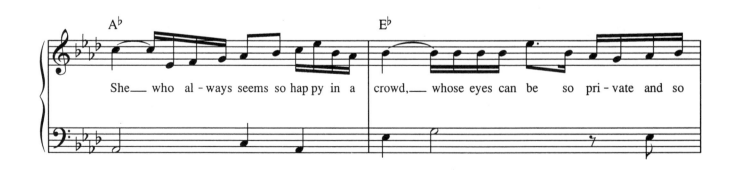

She____ who al - ways seems so hap py in a crowd,____ whose eyes can be so pri - vate and so

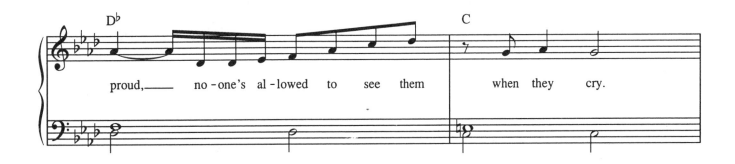

proud,___ no-one's al-lowed to see them when they cry.

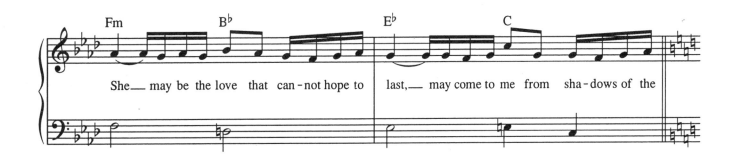

She___ may be the love that can-not hope to last,___ may come to me from sha-dows of the

D.S. al Coda

past___ that I'll re-mem-ber till the day I die.

CODA

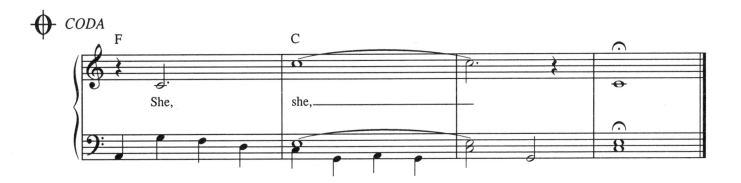

She, she,___

Verse 4:

She may be the reason I survive
The why and wherefore I'm alive
The one I'll care for through the rough and ready years.
Me, I'll take her laughter and her tears
And make them all my souvenirs
For where she goes I've got to be
The meaning of my life is she, she, she.

Somethin' Stupid

Words & Music by C. Carson Parks

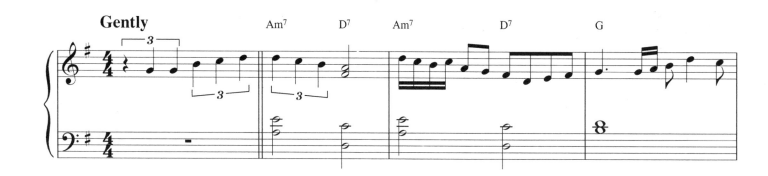

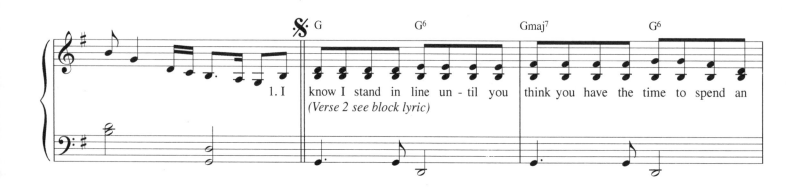

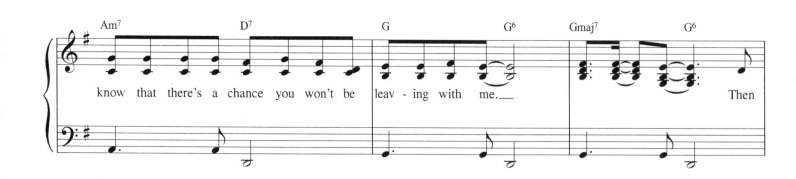

52

Repeat to fade

Verse 2:
I practise every day to find
Some clever lines to say
To make the meaning come true
But then I think I'll wait until
The evening gets late
And I'm alone with you
The time is right
Your perfume fills my head
The stars get red
And oh, the night's so blue
And then I go and spoil it all
By saying somethin' stupid
Like I love you.

Sometimes

Words & Music by Jörgen Elofsson

Moderately slow

mf
1. You tell me you're in love with me,   like you can't take your
2. I don't wan - na be so shy.   Ev - 'ry time that

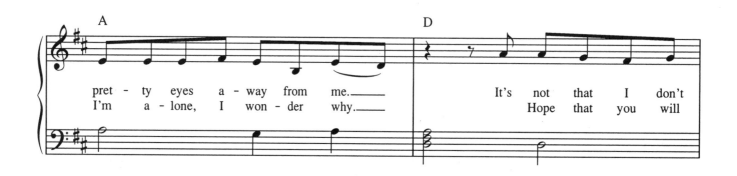

pret - ty eyes a - way from me.   It's not that I don't
I'm a - lone, I won - der why.   Hope that you will

want to stay,   but ev - 'ry time you   come to close, I move a - way.
wait for me,   you'll see   that   you're the on - ly one for me.

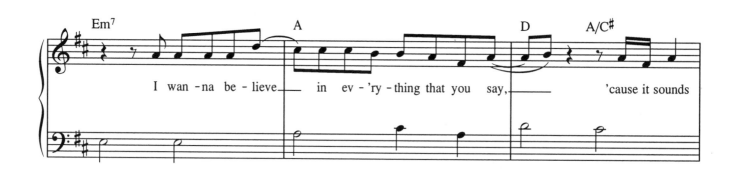

I wan - na be - lieve in ev - 'ry - thing that you say,   'cause it sounds

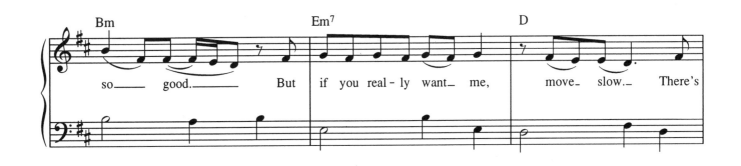

so___ good.___ But if you real - ly want___ me, move___ slow.___ There's

things a - bout me you just have to know.___ Some-times I run,___ some-times

I hide. Some-times I'm scared___ of you.___ But all I real - ly want is to hold___

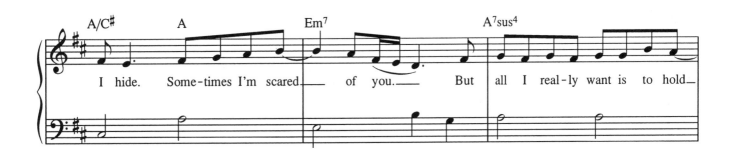

___ you tight,___ treat you right, be with you day___ and night.___

1. Ba - by, all I need is time. **2.** All I real - ly want is to hold___ you tight,___ treat

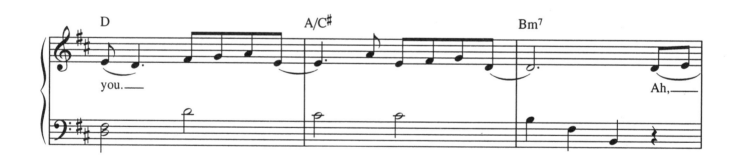

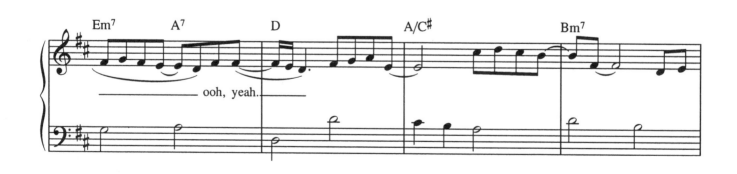

Sing

Words & Music by Fran Healy

Moderately

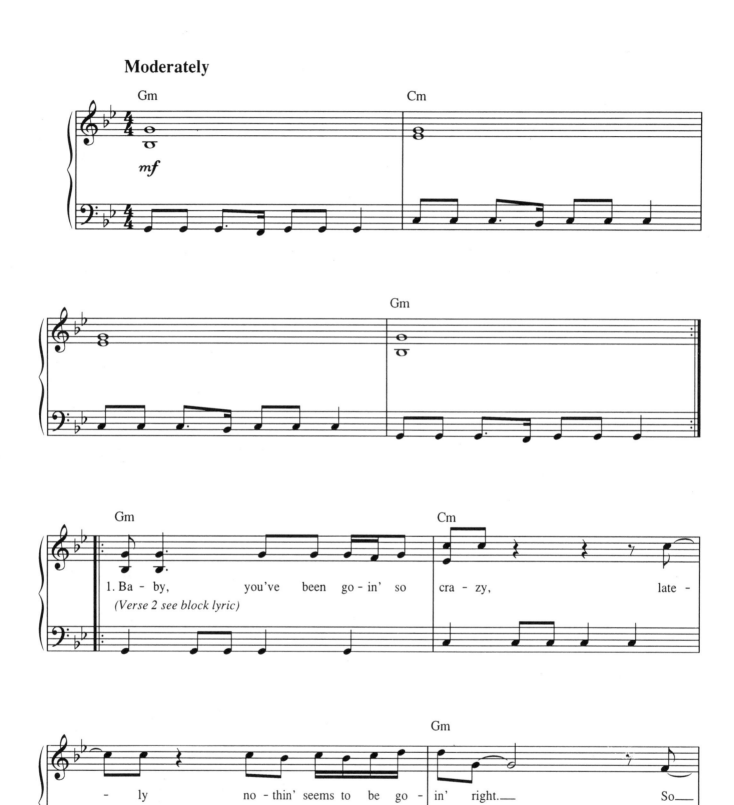

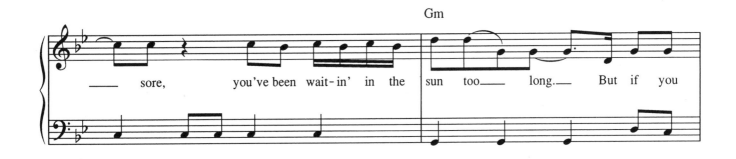

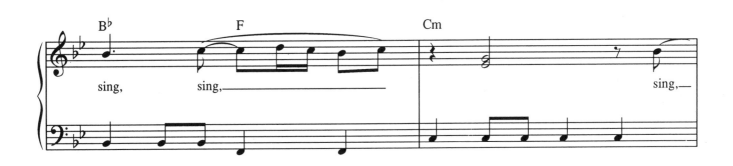

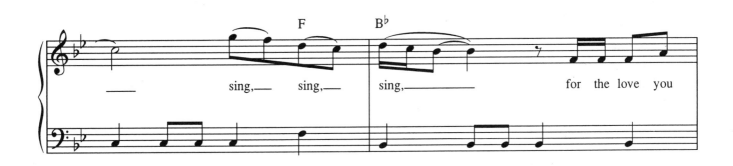

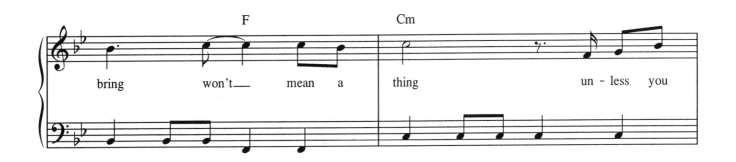

sing,   sing,_____ sing,_____ sing._____   2. Cold_____

Ooh._____

_____   Oh,_____ _____   oh,_____   oh._____

_____   Oh,_____

3. Ba - by,   there's some -thing go - in' wrong   to - day,_____

60

but I say   no -thing,   no -thing,   no -   thing,   no -thing,   no - thing,

no -thing,   no -thing,   no -thing,   no -thing,   no -thing.   So na, na, na, na, now if you sing,—

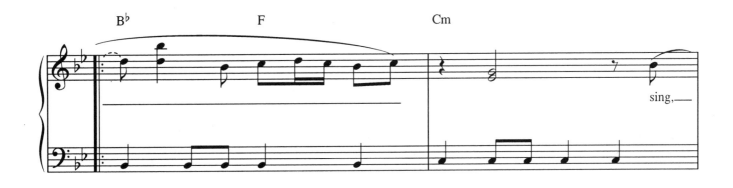

sing,—

—   sing,——   sing,—   sing,———   for the love you

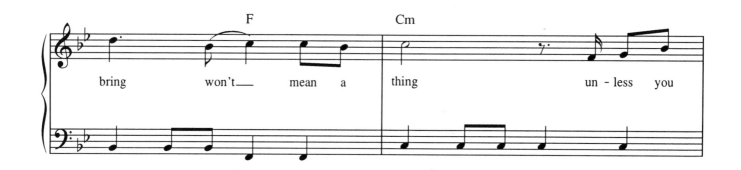

bring   won't   mean a   thing   un - less   you

sing,   sing,   sing,   sing,   sing.   Oh,   ba - by sing,

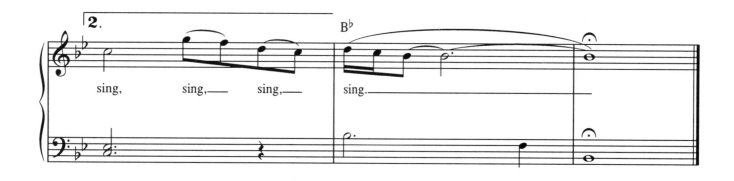

sing,   sing,   sing,   sing.

Verse 2:

Colder, crying over your shoulder
Hold her, tell her everything's gonna be fine
Surely you've been going to hurry
Hurry, 'cause no-one's gonna be stopped.

Not if you sing *etc.*

Take On Me

Words & Music by Morten Harket, Mags Furuholmen & Pat Waaktaar

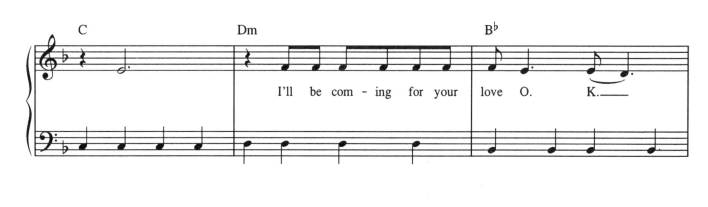

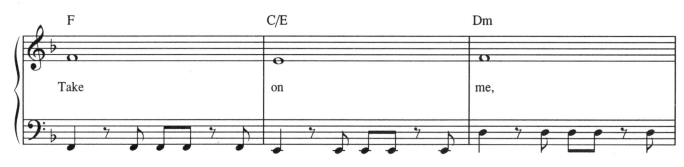

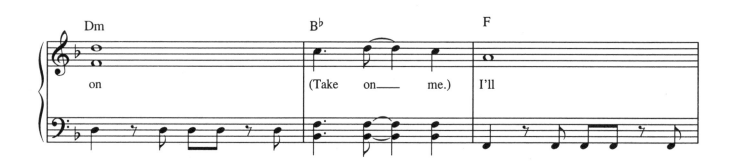

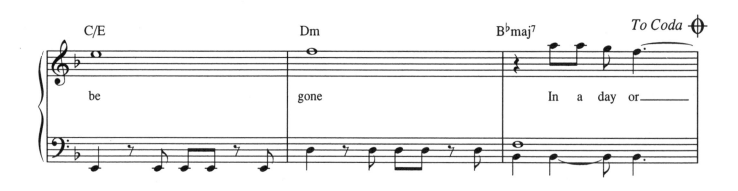

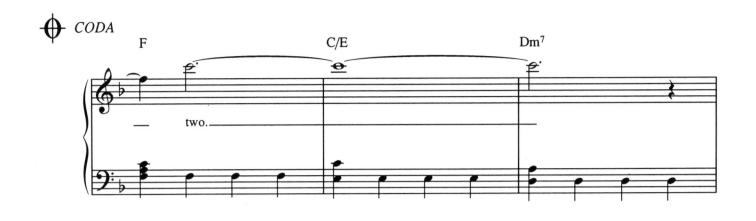

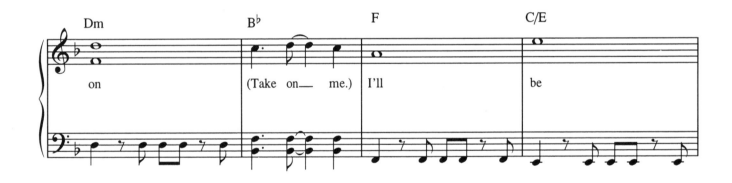

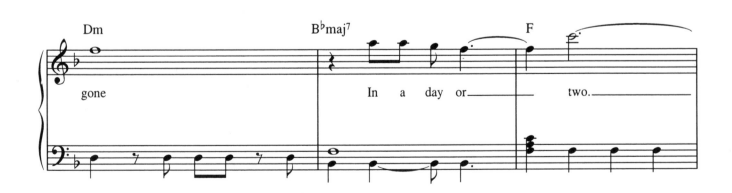

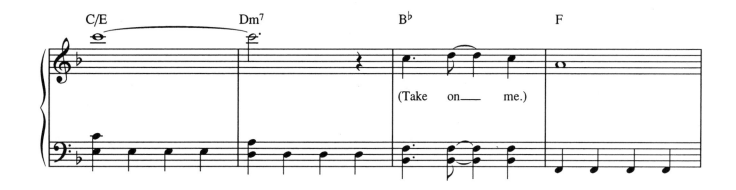

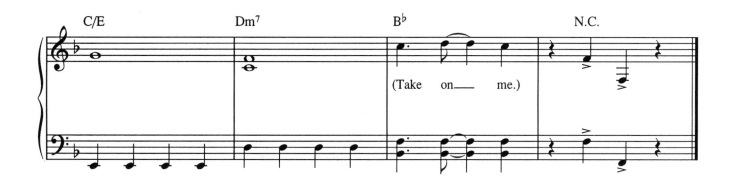

Verse 2:

So needless to say
At odds and ends
But I'll be stumbling away
Slowly learning that life is O.K.
Say after me
It's so much better to be safe than sorry.

Take on me *etc.*

Verse 3:

Oh, things that you say
Yeah, is it a life or
Just to play my worries away
You're all the things I've got to remember
You shyin' away
I'll be coming for you anyway.

Take on me *etc.*

This Year's Love

Words & Music by David Gray

And when you hold me like you do it feels— so— right,— oh now,—

I start to for - get how my heart gets torn when that
(Verse 3 see block lyric)

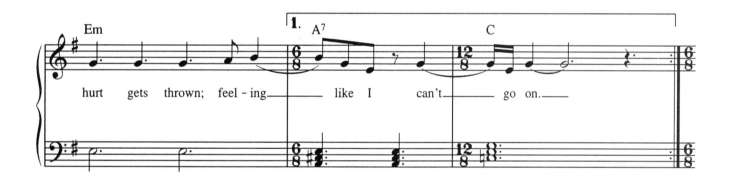

hurt gets thrown; feel - ing— like I can't— go on.—

—dream in - side my— soul, when you kiss me on that mid - night street, sweep me

off my feet, sing-ing_____ ain't this life____ so sweet?____

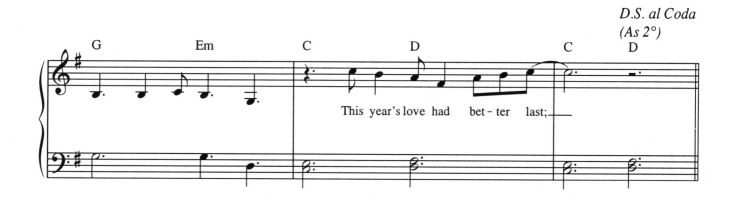

This year's love had bet-ter last;____

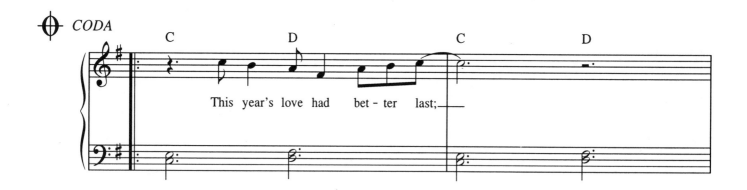

This year's love had bet-ter last;____

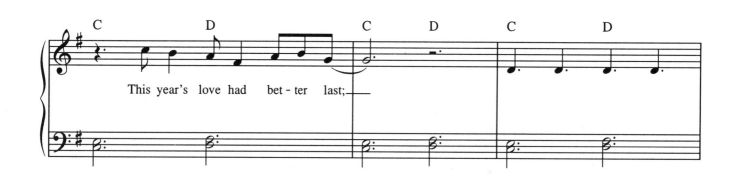

This year's love had bet-ter last;____

This year's love had bet - ter last;

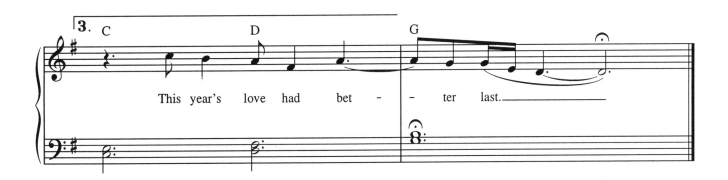

This year's love had bet — — ter last.

Verse 2:

Turning circles and time again
It cuts like a knife, oh now
If you love me I got to know for sure
'Cause it takes something more this time
Than sweet, sweet lies, oh now
Before I open up my arms and fall
Losing all control
Every dream inside my soul
When you kiss me on that midnight street
Sweep me off my feet
Singing ain't this life so sweet.

Verse 3:

'Cause who's to worry if our hearts get torn
When that hurt gets thrown?
Don't you know this life goes on?
Won't you kiss me on that midnight street
Sweep me off my feet
Singing ain't this life so sweet?

Torn

Words & Music by Anne Preven, Scott Cutler & Phil Thornalley

Moderately

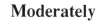

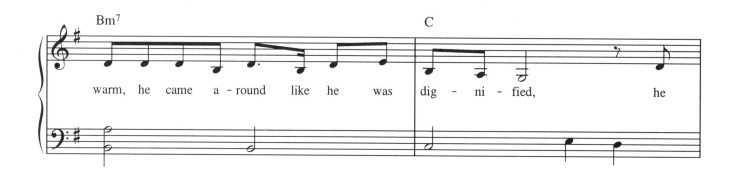

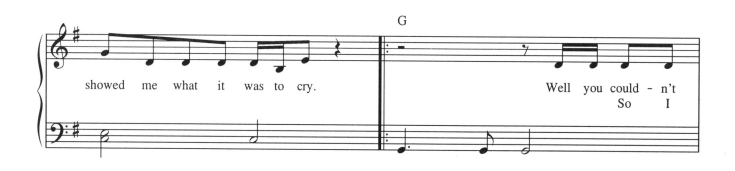

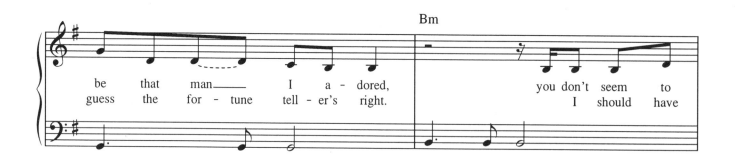

know, don't seem to_____ care what your heart is for but_____
seen just what was there and not some ho - ly light but you

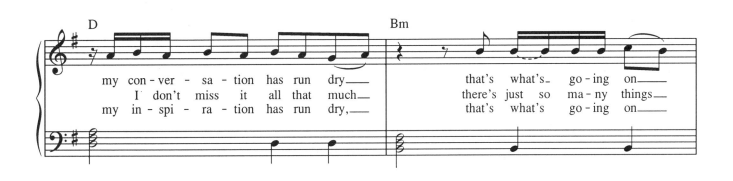

I don't know him a - ny - more, there's no - thing where_____ he used to lie,_____
crawled be - neath my veins and now_____ I don't care_____ I had no luck_____
no - thing where_____ he used to lie,_____

my con - ver - sa - tion has run dry_____ that's what's__ go - ing on_____
I don't miss it all that much_____ there's just so ma - ny things_____
my in - spi - ra - tion has run dry,_____ that's what's go - ing on_____

no - thing's fine, I'm torn.
that I can search, I'm torn. I'm all out of faith, this is how I
no - thing's right, I'm torn. *(See block lyric for* | *final chorus)*

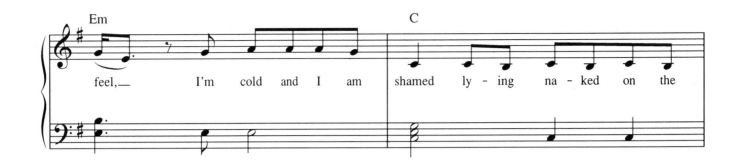

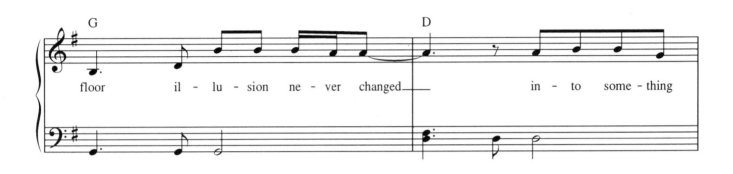

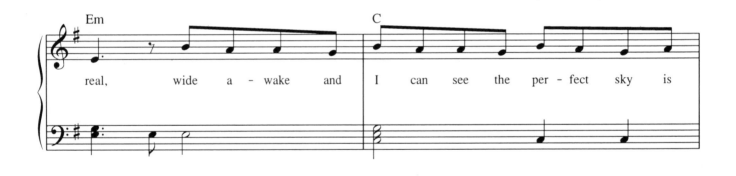

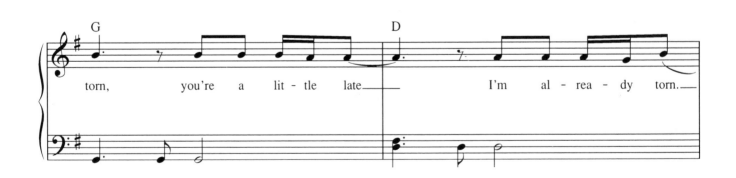

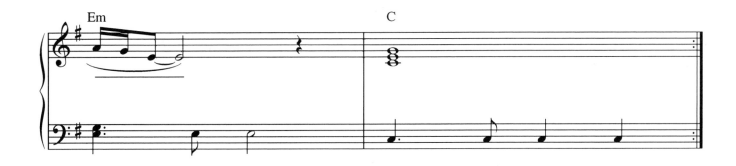

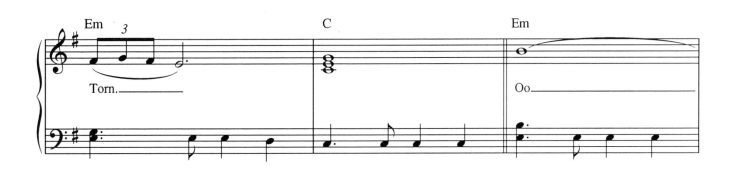

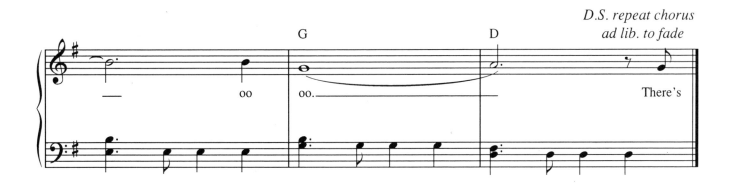

Final Chorus:

I'm all out of faith
This is how I feel
I'm cold and I'm ashamed
Bound and broken on the floor.
You're a little late
I'm already torn
Torn.

Trouble

Words & Music by Guy Berryman, Jon Buckland, Will Champion & Chris Martin

Moderately slow

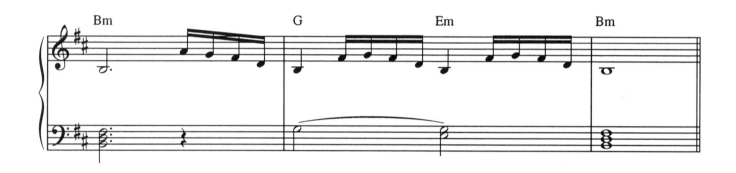

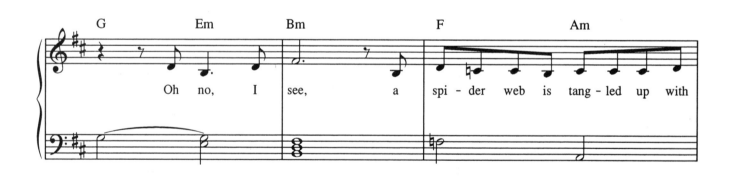

Oh no, I see, a spi - der web is tang - led up with me. I lost my head and thought of all the stu - pid things I've

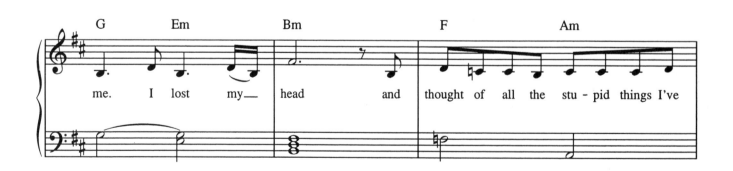

me. I lost my head and thought of all the stu - pid things I've

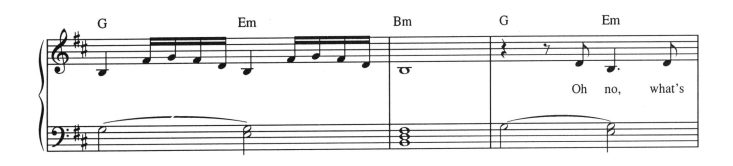

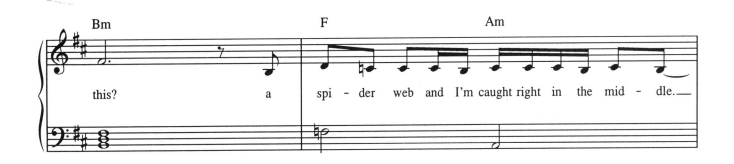

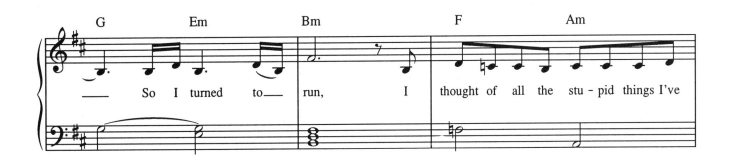

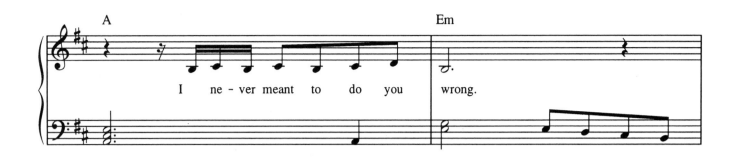

I ne-ver meant to do you wrong.

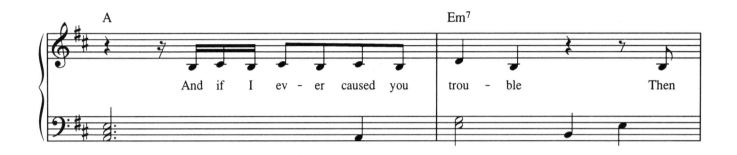

And if I ev – er caused you trou – ble Then

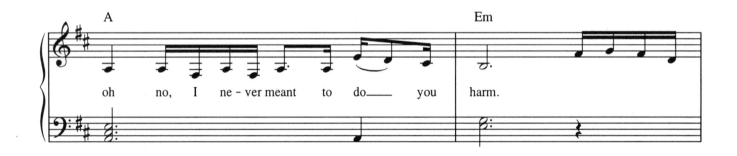

oh no, I ne-ver meant to do____ you harm.

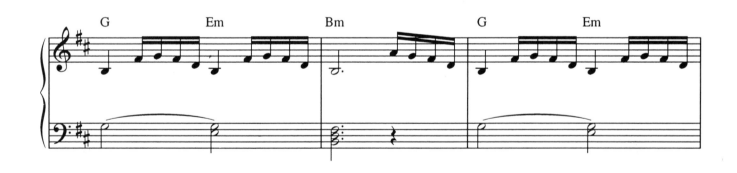

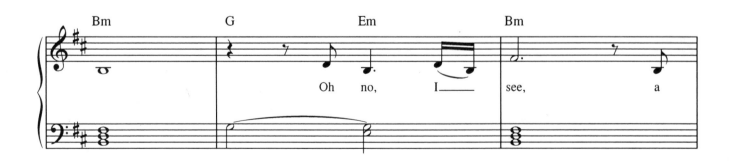

Oh no, I____ see, a

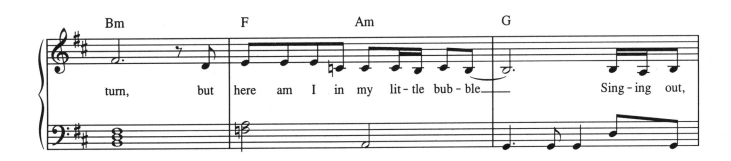

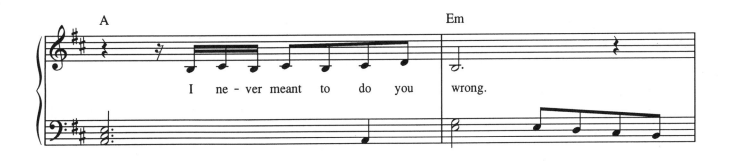

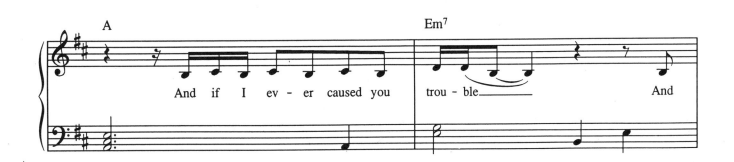

ah,   no, I ne - ver meant to do____ you harm.

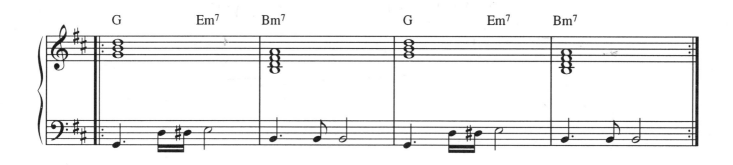

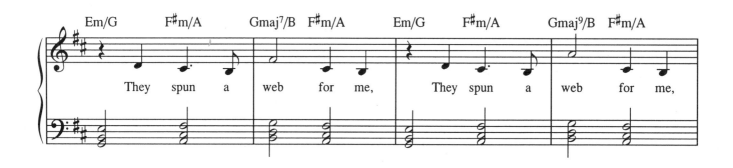

They spun a web for me,   They spun a web for me,

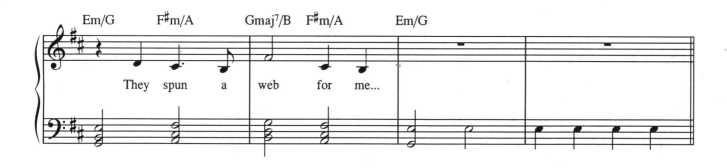

They spun a web for me...

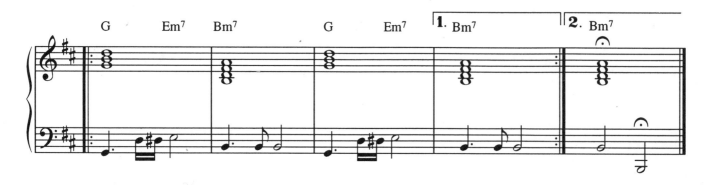

Unchained Melody

Words by Hy Zaret
Music by Alex North

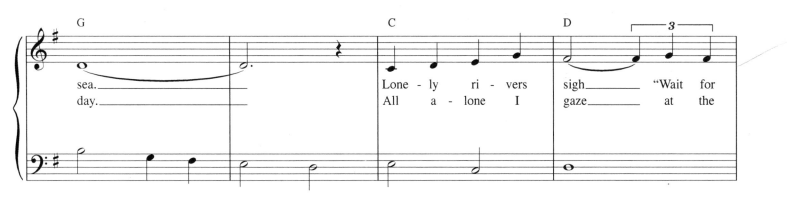

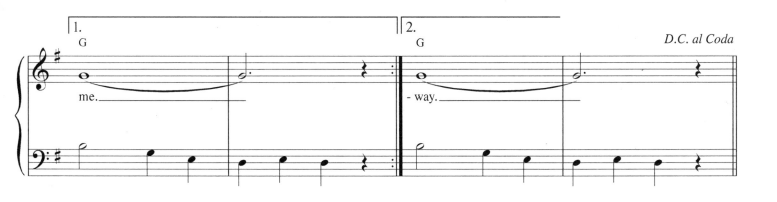

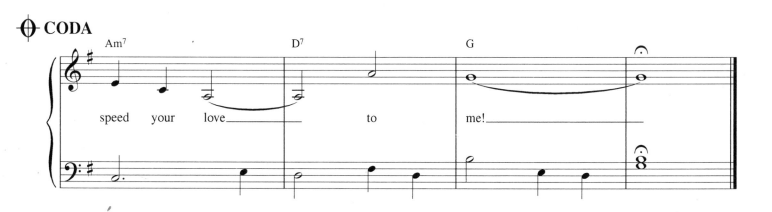

Whole Again

Words & Music by Stuart Kershaw, Andy McCluskey, Bill Padley & Jeremy Godfrey

Moderately

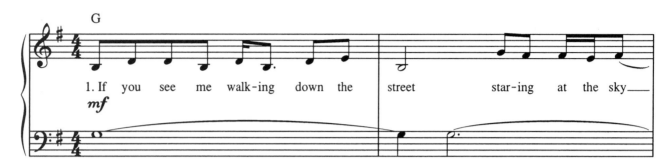

1. If you see me walk-ing down the street star-ing at the sky

and drag-ging my two feet, you just pass me by, it still makes me

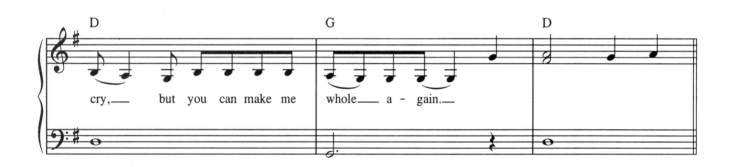

cry, but you can make me whole a - gain.

2. If you see me with a - no-ther man laugh - ing and jo -

(Verse 2 see block lyric)

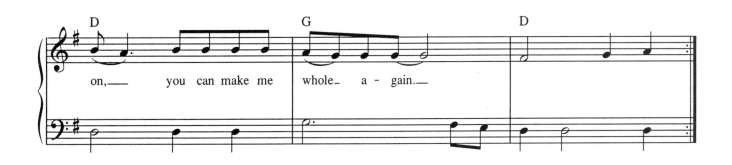

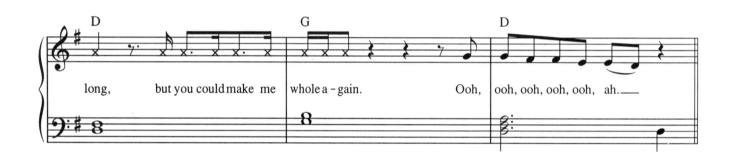

one, you still turn me on, you can make me whole a - gain.

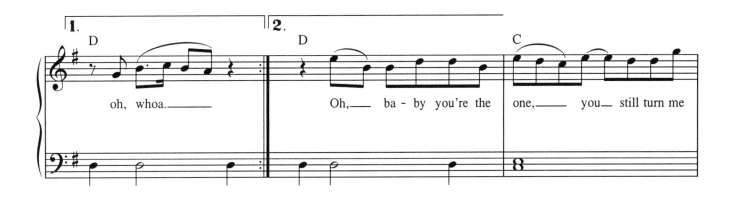

1. oh, whoa.

2. Oh, ba - by you're the one, you still turn me

on, you can make me whole a - gain.

Verse 2:

Time is laying heavy on my heart
Seems I've got too much of it since we've been apart
My friends make me smile, if only for a while
You can make me whole again.

You've Got A Friend In Me
(from Walt Disney's 'Toy Story')

Music & Lyrics by Randy Newman

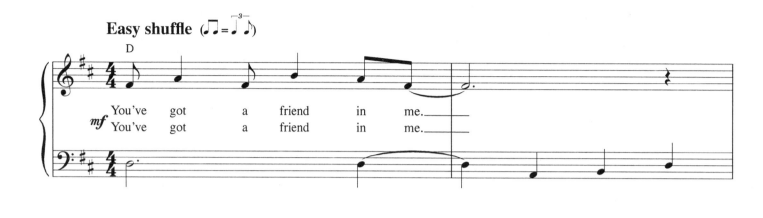

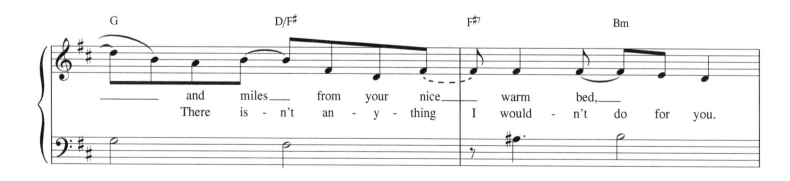

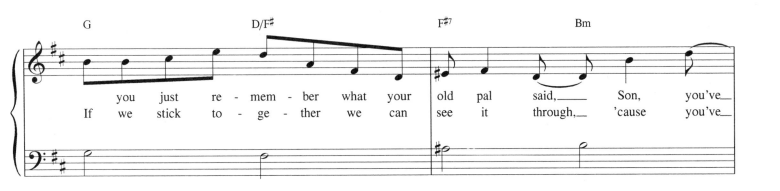

you just re-mem-ber what your old pal said,___ Son, you've___
If we stick to-ge-ther we can see it through,___ 'cause you've___

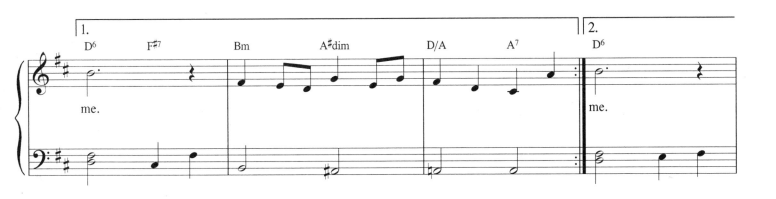

___ got a friend in me.___ Yeah, you've___ got a friend in
___ got a friend in me.___ Yeah, you've___ got a friend in

1.
me.

2.
me.

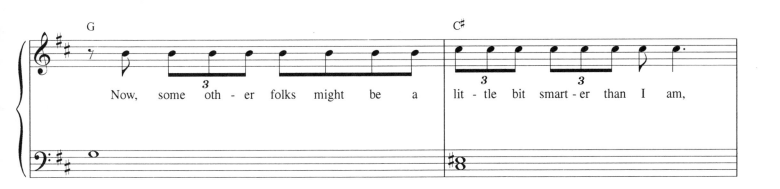

Now, some oth-er folks might be a lit-tle bit smart-er than I am,

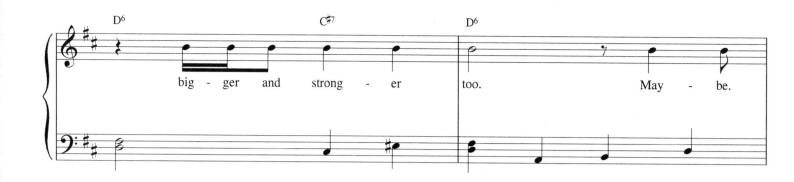

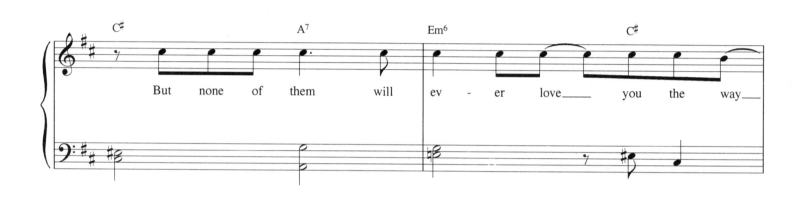

90

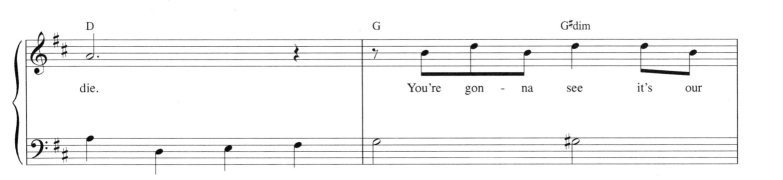

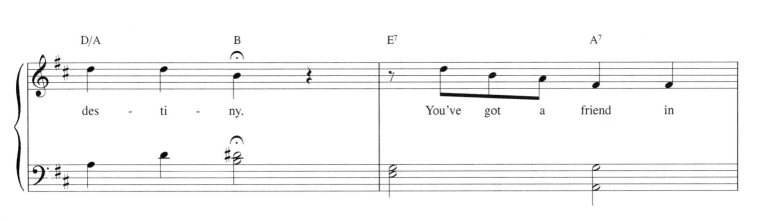

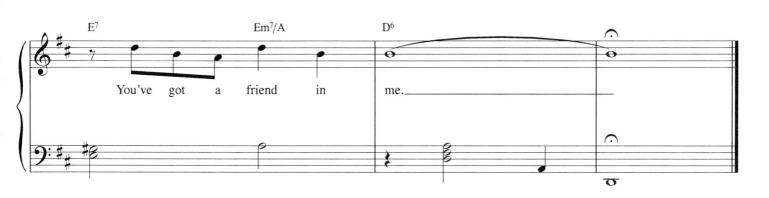

World Of Our Own

Words & Music by Steve Mac & Wayne Hector

Moderate/Slow

1. You make me feel fun - ny, *(Verse 2 see block lyric)* when

you come a - round,_ yeah, that's what I found_ out, hon - ey. What am I

do - ing with - out_ you? You make me feel hap - py, when I

What am I do-ing with-out___ you? All of the things I've been___ look-ing for have

al - ways been here out - side___ of my door, and all of the time I'm look - ing for some - thing

new. (World of___ our own.)_____ new, what am I do-ing with - out___ you?___

Verse 2:
Well I guess I'm ready
For settling down
And fooling around is over
And I swear that it's true
No buts or maybe's
When I'm falling down
There's always someone saves me
And girl it's you
Funny how life can
Be so surprising
I'm just realising what you do.

We got a little world of our own   *etc.*